Scamp at the Dog Show

Join the sets of dogs to the correct numb

How many dogs in each set?

1 2 3 4 5

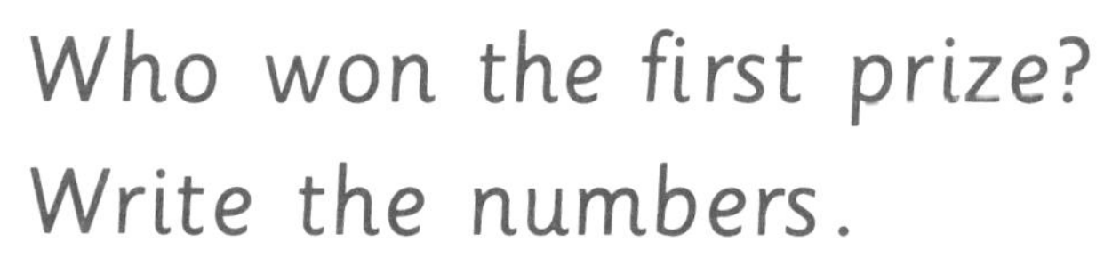

Who won the first prize?

Write the numbers.

Scamp goes on holiday.

He takes 2 of everything – just in case!

Make 2.

Write 2.

undation

Schofield & Sims

Nursery Numbers 2

Name ____

Numbers 1 to 5

Help Scamp write the numbers.

Match the sets to the correct number.

2

3

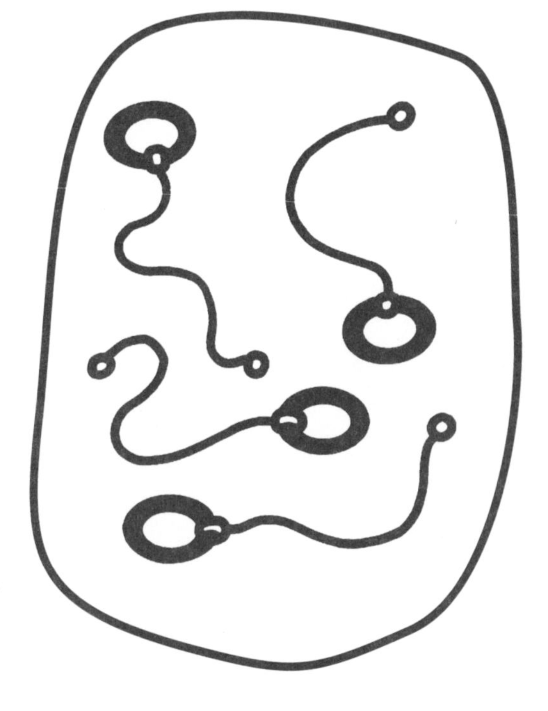

4

5

What does Scamp see on holiday?

He sees 3 of everything!

Make 3.

Write 3.

3 3 3 3

Scamp is at the fair.

Today he sees 4 of everything.

Make 4.

Write 4.

Scamp visits the park.

5

There are 5 of everything.

Make 5.

Write 5.

Writing numbers

Scamp can't decide what to eat first!

Match the plates to the correct number.

1

2

3

4

5

What is Scamp doing?

Colour the shapes.

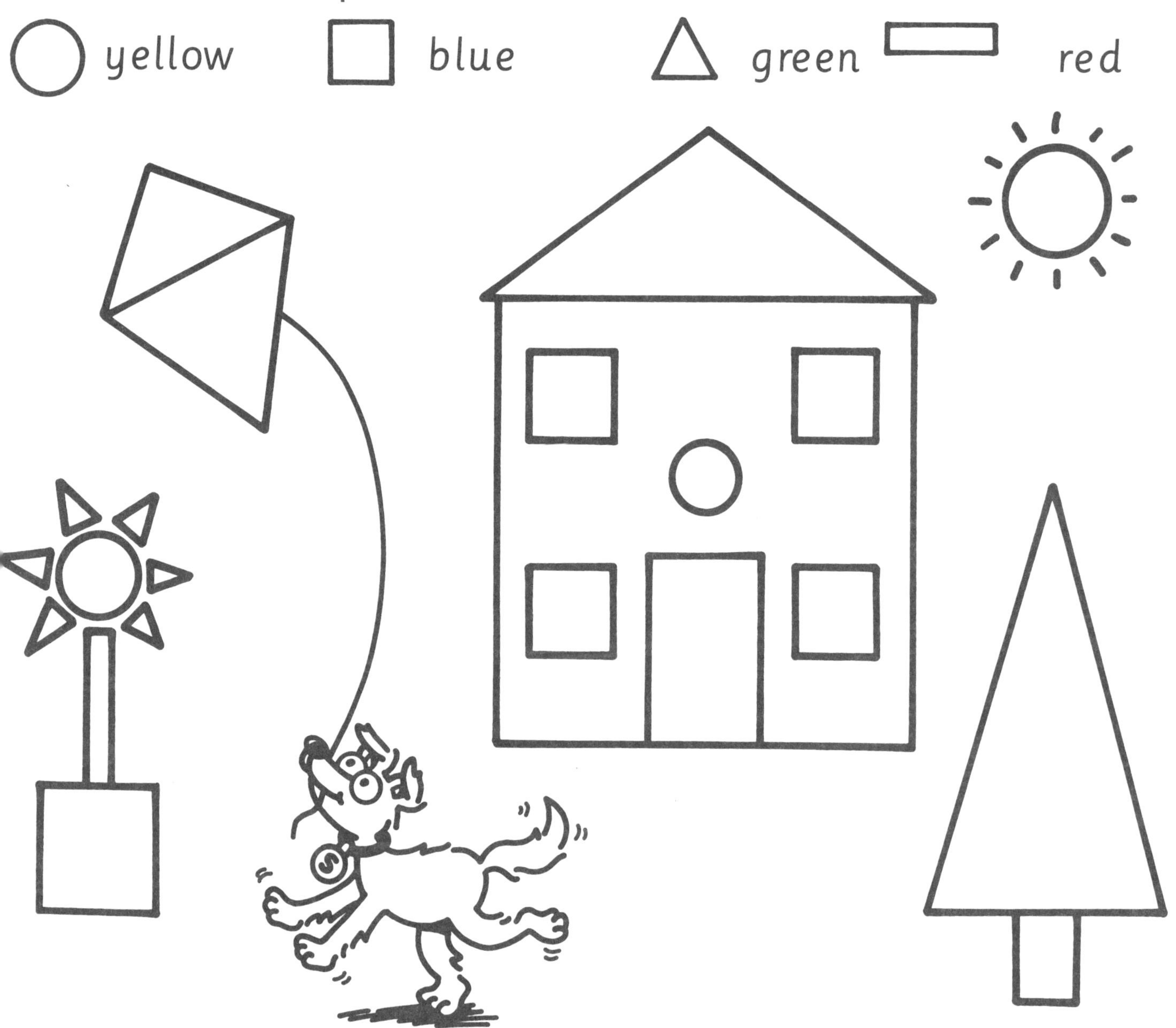

Collect some shapes to draw round to make a picture.

Where is Scamp now?

Join the dots to find out.

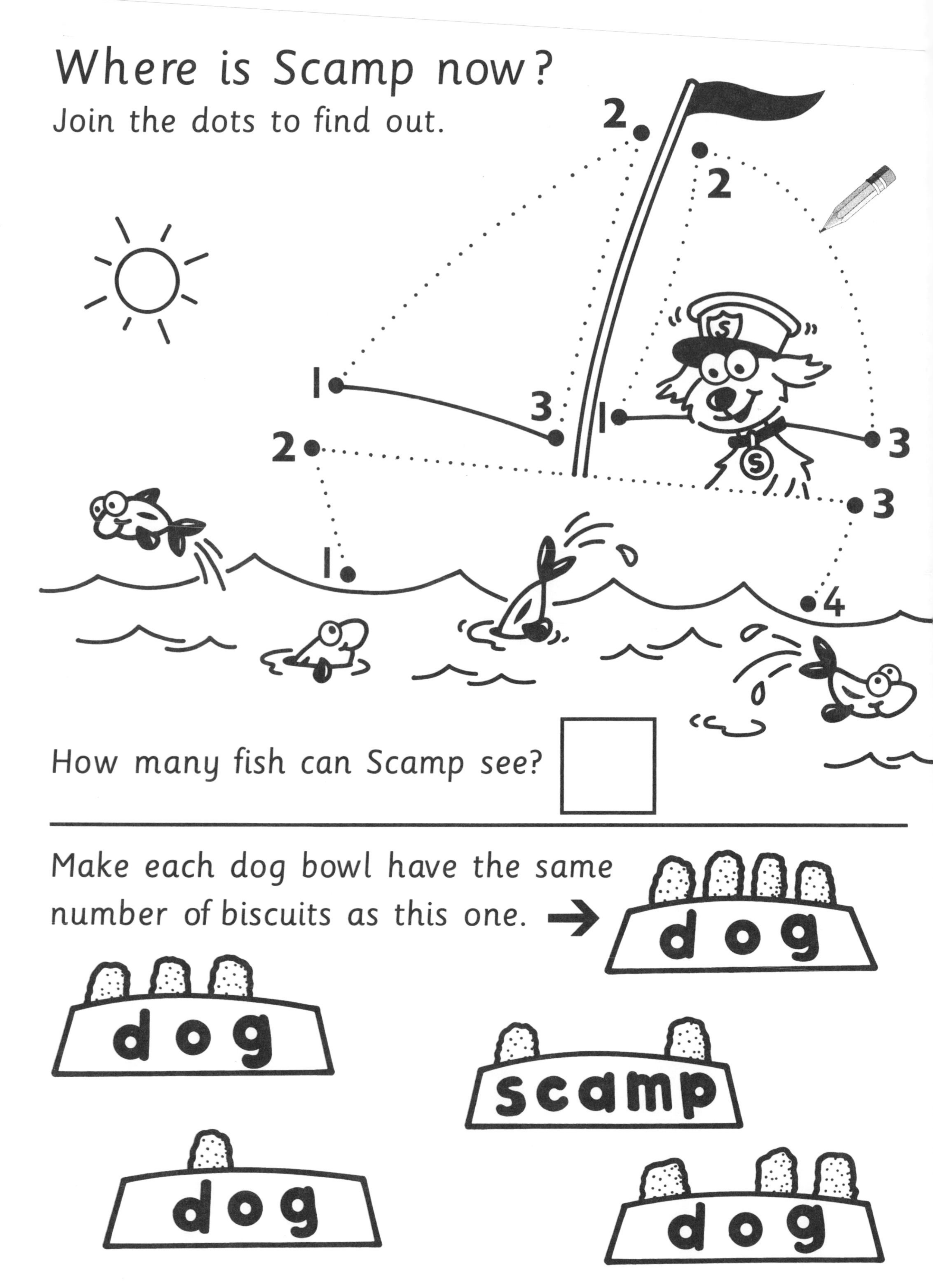

How many fish can Scamp see?

Make each dog bowl have the same number of biscuits as this one. →

Which is Scamp's bowl? Colour it red.

Can you see Scamp?

Draw the next thing in each pattern.

Make Scamp's friends have the same number of spots as Rosie. →

Scamp is busy.

Help him! Draw the correct number.

Write 2.

2 2 2 2 2

Colour 2 things on each line.

What is Scamp doing today?

You can help him. Draw the correct number.

Write 3.

Colour 3 things on each line.

Which will Scamp enjoy eating most?

Whose birthday is it?

Help Scamp to blow the candles out and unwrap his presents. How old is Scamp? Count his presents.

Write 4.

What presents did Scamp have for his birthday?
Colour 4 things on each line.

Scamp is at the circus.

Draw 5 juggling balls.

Draw 5 custard pies.

Write 5.

Colour 5 things on each line.

Scamp visits the farm.

Help him count the animals.

How many did Scamp see? Write the numbers.

Where is Scamp?

Join the dots to find out.

Draw 5 birds in the sky.

Scamp goes for a walk.

Who does he meet? Colour red the house with 5 windows.

How many?

Draw

1 door

4 windows

2 chimneys

Scamp is at the market.

Count the fruit he buys.

Ring the correct number in each row.

Write the numbers.

Highest

Colour the highest one.

Draw a higher flag pole.

Write a number on your flag.

Lowest

Colour the lowest one.

Draw a lower jump for Scamp.

Thickest

Colour the thickest.

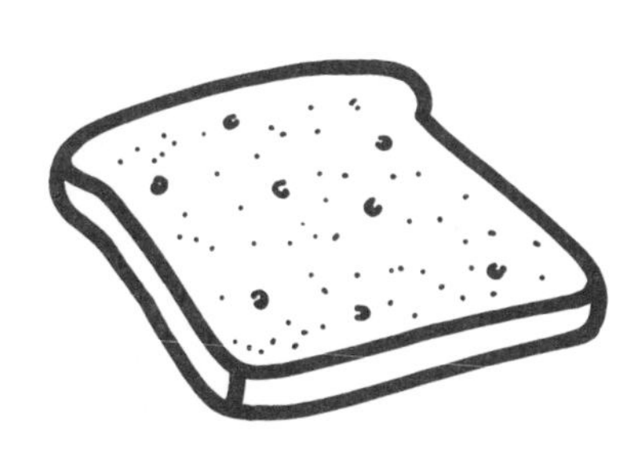

Draw a thicker pencil.

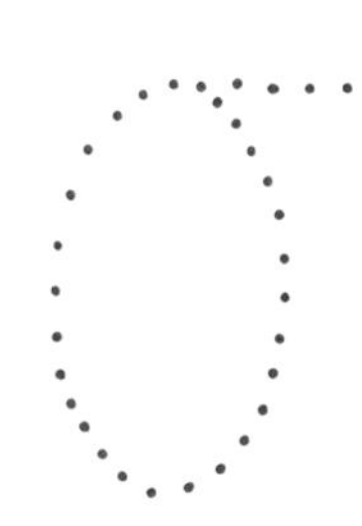

Thinner

Colour the thinnest. What is Scamp doing?

Draw a thinner snake.

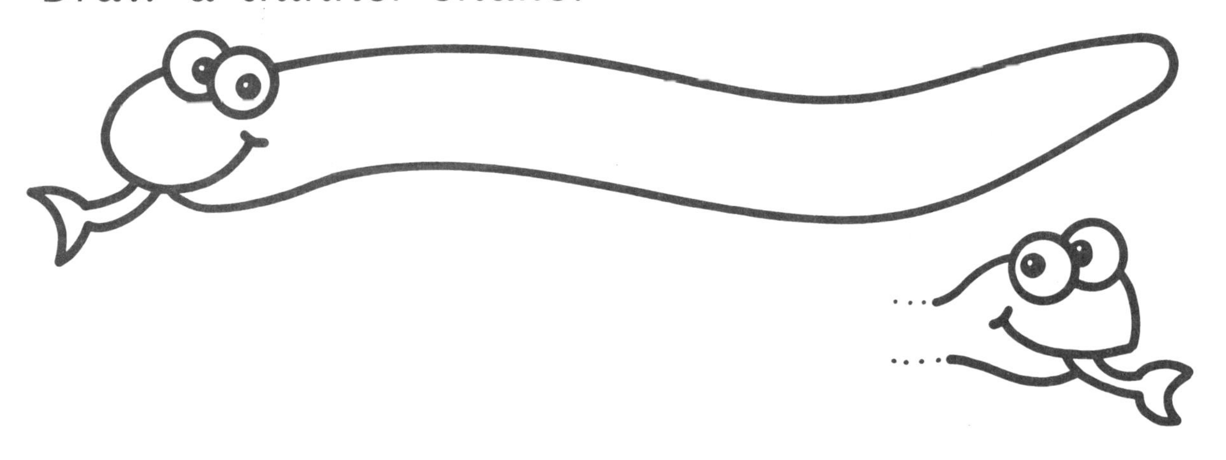

Schofield&Sims

the long-established educational publisher specialising in maths, English and science

Nursery Numbers is a series of graded activity books that reinforce mathematical language and early number skills, including matching, sequencing and counting. The books cover concepts such as money, shapes and measures and feature the appealing character of **Scamp the dog**.

Nursery Numbers Book 2 includes:

- Numbers to 5
- Common 2-D shapes
- Comparative size (for example, higher/lower and thicker/thinner).

The full range of titles in the series is as follows:

Nursery Numbers Book 1:	ISBN 978 07217 0867 6
Nursery Numbers Book 2:	ISBN 978 07217 0868 3
Nursery Numbers Book 3:	ISBN 978 07217 0869 0
Nursery Numbers Book 4:	ISBN 978 07217 0870 6
Nursery Numbers Book 5:	ISBN 978 07217 0906 2
Nursery Numbers Book 6:	ISBN 978 07217 0907 9

Have you tried **Nursery Writing** by Schofield & Sims?
This series uses **Eddy the teddy** to help young children learn letters, sounds and simple words.

For further information and to place your order visit www.schofieldandsims.co.uk or telephone 01484 607080

First edition copyright © Schofield and Sims Ltd, 2001
Sixteenth impression 2016
Author: Sally Johnson

Printed in India by Multivista Global Pvt. Ltd

ISBN 978-07217-0868-3

ISBN 978 07217 0868 3

£2.45
(Retail price)

Schofield&Sims
Dogley Mill, Fenay Bridge, Huddersfield HD8 0NQ
Phone: 01484 607080 Facsimile: 01484 606815
E-mail: sales@schofieldandsims.co.uk

Early Years Foundation Stage
Age range: 3–5 years